A Suitably Happy Ending

PERFORMANCE PLAYS

BEGINNER

Alison Chaplin

AUTHOR
Alison Chaplin

EDITOR
Steven Carruthers

ASSISTANT EDITOR
Roanne Davis

SERIES DESIGNER
Anna Oliwa/Heather Sanneh

DESIGNER
Anna Oliwa

ILLUSTRATIONS
Emma Ward
COVER ARTWORK
Jackie Raynor

Text © 2000 Alison Chaplin
© 2000 Scholastic Ltd

Designed using Adobe Pagemaker

Published by Scholastic Ltd,
Villiers House,
Clarendon Avenue,
Leamington Spa,
Warwickshire CV32 5PR

1 2 3 4 5 6 7 8 9 0   0 1 2 3 4 5 6 7 8 9

British Library Cataloguing-in-Publication
Data. A catalogue record for this book is
available from the British Library.

ISBN 0-439-01684-3

ACKNOWLEDGEMENTS

First performed in Manchester by
participants on the 'Drama and
Theatre Workshop' in August 1996,
and again in October 1999. Many
thanks to all the children for their
suggestions of script changes and
enthusiastic performances!

For permission to give a performance
of this play at which an admission
charge is made, please contact the
Editorial Department, Educational
Books, Scholastic Limited, Villiers
House, Clarendon Avenue,
Leamington Spa, Warks., CV32 5PR.
You do not need to seek permission if
you do not charge an entry fee for the
performance. Performing licences
must be applied for prior to beginning
rehearsals.

Fees are £10.00 per performance for
a paying audience of up to 200 people
and £15.00 per performance for
paying audiences of 200 people or
over.

*Alison Chaplin is the drama consultant
for the Borough of Stockport and
manager of 'Arts on the Move', a
company specializing in providing a
range of drama and theatre services. For
information call 0161 881 0868.*

CONTENTS LIST

INTRODUCTION

A Suitably Happy Ending

USING THIS BOOK

The aim of this *Scholastic Performance Play* is to provide teachers with the appropriate resources to read, rehearse and perform short plays. This book enables teachers and children to understand the process of interpreting scripts and the approaches needed for successful rehearsals and performances. From providing pre-rehearsal support to supplying linking reading and writing tasks, the book is structured in a way that assumes no prior knowledge of script work and no previous experience of staging performances, leading those involved through the process in easy-to-follow stages.

WORKSHOP SESSIONS

Workshop sessions are provided to help the teacher to introduce the children to the concept of drama. The sessions help the children to:

- read and understand playscripts
- explore the implicit themes and issues within the play
- appreciate character development
- learn the relevant skills required for performance.

Each session is structured to approach a different aspect of working with a playscript, using methods which are both practical and enjoyable.

PLAYSCRIPT

The playscript is organized in an easy-to-follow format, complete with full stage directions and scene changes. At the beginning of each script, following the cast list, there is a brief outline of each character which provides an indication of behavioural traits and helps children to understand how that role should be performed. Most of the plays in the *Performance Plays* series are simple to stage and require little in the way of make-up, costume or setting.

PRODUCTION SUPPORT

These notes provide practical advice to support the teacher from the beginning to the end of the performance process, including: holding auditions; structuring rehearsals; ideas for simple and effective staging; props, costumes and make-up; and finally, presenting professional 'curtain calls'. The ideas provided have arisen from the author's own experience of directing this play and are thus informed by a knowledge of what has worked in practice. However, they are not meant to be completely prescriptive: if teachers feel that they have the resources, time and skills to create more elaborate staging and costumes, or to approach the performance in a different way, then they should feel free to do so!

LITERACY SUPPORT

This section at the end of the book is directly linked to the requirements of the National Literacy Strategy *Framework for Teaching*. It provides suggestions for supportive tasks, organized under the headings of 'Story'; 'Characters'; 'Theme'; 'Working with playscript layout'; and 'Performance-related tasks'. Again, these ideas are not intended to be prescriptive, but aim to provide teachers with examples of how the playscript can be used to generate structured literacy work.

A FLEXIBLE RESOURCE

The unique aspect of these *Performance Plays* is that their contents can be utilized in a number of different ways: as a simple reading resource, to provide a basis for literacy tasks, to introduce children to the concept of performance drama, or to produce a full-scale school production. Readers should feel free to employ the book in any way which meets their needs. However, the most important approach for anyone using it is to be flexible, enthusiastic, and prepared to 'have a go'!

GUIDANCE FOR WORKING WITH SCRIPTS

If the children have no previous experience of script work, it is suggested that you lead them through the following simple drama process to make them familiar with the style and concept of scripted performance.

Ask the children (in their classroom places) to find a partner and hold a conversation with him or her. It could be about anything: the television programmes they watched the night before, their favourite books, what they did during the school holidays, and so on. Allow these conversations to run for about a minute and then ask the children to stop talking.

Now ask the pairs to label themselves 'A' and 'B'. Tell them that they must hold a conversation again, but this time 'B' cannot respond until 'A' has finished talking (or until 'A' has finished a sentence, if 'A' is going on for too long). Insist that the children adhere to this procedure for speaking and responding, as this forms the basis for most scripted formats.

Allow these structured conversations to run for about a minute, then ask the children to stop talking. Invite them to give feedback on the type of conversations they had. Using the board, write their statements and responses in the form of an 'A said' and 'B said' structure:

A said: ....
B said: ....

Record just a couple of lines from each conversation, to show the children how these conversations can be recorded. Ask them to suggest how their second conversations were different from their first ones. Answers should include: that they had names ('A' and 'B'), that they could only speak when the other person had finished speaking, that the conversations were not as natural, that they had to listen more carefully and think more about what they said and how they responded to their partners.

Now ask the children to join with another pair to make a four. (Odd numbers or unequal groups are also acceptable.) Ask them to hold an initial unstructured conversation with each other about a subject of your choosing: leave these to run for about a minute. Then ask the children to label themselves 'A', 'B', 'C' and 'D', (match letters of the alphabet with the numbers in each group accordingly) and to hold another conversation, this time following the same restriction as before: while someone in the group is talking, no-one else can speak. Tell the children that they do not necessarily have to join in the conversation in alphabetical order.

Invite feedback about these conversations. Again, ask for comments on how the second discussion differed from the first. Record part of a structured conversation on the board, using 'A', 'B', 'C' and 'D' to indicate who speaks which lines.

Inform the children that this is how plays are structured: they are written records of people speaking to each other, having conversations or discussions; that the name of the character speaking is indicated at the beginning of each piece of dialogue.

Further practice for the children could include:

● Writing down their own conversations in script form, using the 'A' and 'B', or 'A', 'B', 'C', 'D' format.
● Devising and writing original conversations, using the 'A' and 'B' or 'A', 'B', 'C', 'D' format.
● Lifting a section of dialogue from a familiar story and recording it in scripted form.
● Rewriting their own conversations, using recognizable names instead of letters of the alphabet.
● Improvising a specific scene (such as someone buying an item in a shop), recording this improvisation using a tape recorder or Dictaphone, then replaying the recording in order to transpose it as a written script.

The main aim is to enable children to appreciate that a playscript is simply dialogue, conversations or verbal statements written down, and that the format gives a clear indication of who is speaking at any one time. Advise the children that characters may interrupt each other, but that two people will never talk at the same time during a scripted performance: the lines will always be spoken in sequence.

Ensure that the children understand that, unlike other written speech, script texts do not contain speech marks or quotation marks because the whole text is known and understood to be speech and so they are unnecessary.

Go on from this exercise to reading and discussing an extract from any playscript: explore how the text indicates who is speaking, analyse the sequencing of the dialogue and reaffirm the concept of characters speaking in turn.

As a final note, when reading the playscript in this book, ask the children to suggest what the purpose of the words in brackets or italic may be. They may reply: 'How characters say things', 'What characters do' or 'How characters do things'. Keep the language as simple as this initially, developing the children's vocabulary gradually as they become more familiar with reading and understanding scripts. (See 'Literacy support' on page 48.)

THEMES AND ISSUES IN THE PLAY

A Suitably Happy Ending provides teachers with the opportunity to explore both a particular style of writing and a variety of issues which arise from the play text. The original aim of the play was to explore the genre of fairy tales and the archetypical characters which are usually employed within that type of story. The play, therefore, includes a number of recognizable fairy tale characters, from goblins and evil witches to kindly saviours and the beleaguered hero.

Although a gentle comedy, the play can be used to highlight more serious issues, such as the consequences of arguing or fighting with others; being part of a gang, and the concept of good triumphing over evil – which leads to the 'suitably happy ending'!

Whilst the Goblins and Witches are not inherently 'evil', they are not 'good' people either, and the dreadful consequences of their tribal antagonism should be used to highlight the fact that using violence to resolve arguments is doomed to failure.

The character of Jack appears as more of an anti-hero than a regular fairy story champion. In making him an outcast for failing his SATs, but an achiever all the same, the play emphasizes that the concept of success can take many forms. At first glance it may appear that all of the 'good' characters in this play could be defined as unintelligent, but the 'bad' characters are not 'overbright' either! This helps to emphasize that being pleasant and considerate to others is just as important as being considered clever, if not more so, and the play text could be seen to focus upon this moral.

These sessions should take place before any rehearsals or practical application of the playscript. They introduce the children to drama and theatre, develop their speaking and listening skills, increase their level of concentration, help to prepare them for the types of activity they will be doing during work on the playscript, and develop their ability to perform confidently and effectively and generate positive group interaction.

SESSION 1:
INTRODUCTORY WARM-UP

Timing: Spend no more than 10 minutes on each individual activity. The whole session should take no more than 40 minutes.

Resources: A large space (such as the school hall), whistle, chairs (optional).

Objectives: To introduce the children to the concept of drama, to encourage children to respond appropriately to instructions, to promote positive group interaction.

WITCHES AND GOBLINS

A PHYSICAL WARM-UP

Divide the children into two teams. Name one team 'the Witches' and the other 'the Goblins'. Explain that you are dividing up the space so that each team has a 'safety zone' at each end. Stand the teams in two lines facing one another about three feet apart in the middle of the space.

Explain that when you say, 'I know a really wicked... Witch', all the Witches must chase the Goblins as they run back to their safety zone. But when you say, 'I know a really wicked... Goblin', the Goblins chase the Witches back to their safety zone. Any children who are tagged by the opposing team join that team for the next round of the game. They remain on that team until they are tagged again by the opposition. Always start each new round of the game with both teams lined up facing each other quietly. Continue until either exhaustion sets in, or the teams are too uneven for a fair game.

Then ask the children to stand in a circle facing inwards, and move on to...

LOOK DOWN, LOOK UP

DEVELOPS CONCENTRATION AND GROUP INTERACTION

Explain to the children that when they hear you instruct them to 'Look down!', they are to look at the floor. Tell them that then, when they hear you say 'Look up!', they are to lift their heads and make direct eye contact with another person standing in the circle. Advise the children that they are to make eye contact immediately when they hear you say 'Look up!'.

Inform the children that they must look directly at someone else standing in the circle and must not change their eye direction once they have looked up. Explain that, if the person they are looking at when they raise their head is also looking at them, both players are 'out' and must sit down. These players take no further part in the game.

The instructions to 'Look down' and 'Look up' are then repeated, with children making direct eye contact with someone else standing in the circle.

Children can choose anyone in the circle to look at each time. Play the game in silence. Continue repeating the instructions until the majority of players are 'out' and you have a winner or winners. Repeat the game as required, then ask the children to stand in a space, and move on to...

MOOD FREEZES

INTRODUCES PERFORMANCE SKILLS AND DEVELOPS LISTENING SKILLS

Ask the children to walk around the room carefully, without bumping or touching each other. Advise them to listen out for your whistle. After a short time, blow the whistle, shout out a number, and tell the children to get into a group of that number as quickly as they can. (You may wish to choose a number which will divide the class evenly, or encourage individual work by choosing the number 'one'!)

When they are in groups, call out a mood or emotion, (such as 'happiness'), and tell them to make a shape or image with their bodies which represents that emotion. (Or anger, fear, sadness, boredom, loneliness – it is up to you, but all the children should represent the same mood or emotion.)

Advise the children that they can represent the mood in an abstract way, such as by shaping their bodies into 'happy' positions, or they can represent the mood in a realistic way, such as by creating an image of people being happy.

Count down from ten whilst they prepare their shapes, and on the count of one, shout 'Freeze!' (Give no countdown if children are working individually.) Insist on stillness and silence. Go around looking at all the shapes and images. Comment positively on them, praising in particular those children who are 'freezing' well or expressively. Tell the children to relax, and to begin walking around the room again as before.

Repeat the exercise, blowing the whistle, using another number and a different mood for the 'freeze'. Praise effective freezes each time. Repeat until you sense that the children have had enough. By the end, they should be responding well to the freeze command and should have learned how to represent moods or emotions physically. The freeze method will be used again in a later session. End with...

CIRCLE

CHILDREN REFLECT ON AND EVALUATE THEIR SKILLS

Call the children to sit in a circle, on the floor or on chairs. Ask them whether they enjoyed the drama session or not. Ask for opinions and reasons. What do they think they have learned and achieved from it?

This will give you an indication of any skills and knowledge gained, and can be used as a basis for developing the children's abilities during additional workshop sessions.

SESSION 2:
APPROACHING THE TEXT

Timing: Spend up to 15 minutes on each activity. The whole session should take no more than 60 minutes.

Resources: Copies of the script (one per child), dictionaries, groupings prepared for small-group work, flip chart or board, writing materials, sheet of A3 paper, marker pen.

Objectives: To familiarize children with the play text.

SHARED TEXT WORK

WHOLE-CLASS READING OF THE SCRIPT

Sit with the children in a circle, or with them in their classroom places.

Distribute a copy of the playscript to each child and retain one yourself. If applicable, remind the children of the drama exercise they experienced on understanding scripts (see 'Guidance for working with scripts' on page 5).

Tell the children that now you are all going to read a play called *A Suitably Happy Ending*. Inform them that you will read most of the lines spoken by the characters, but will invite some of them to read the others.

Select two groups of six to eight children and ask one group to speak all of the lines of ALL/ALL OTHER GOBLINS throughout the whole play and the other to speak all of the lines of ALL/ALL OTHER WITCHES. (For support within the groups, make them up of mixed reading ability).

Tell all of the children that they should all read and follow the words in the script whilst they are being read.

Read through the script scene by scene, combining your reading with that of volunteers (or nominees). Read the lines spoken only; do not mention each character name in turn and do not read the stage directions aloud.

One possible distribution of the reading parts is as follows:

- SCENE 1: You read all character lines, except for small groups reading ALL/ALL OTHER GOBLINS and ALL/ALL OTHER WITCHES.
- SCENE 2: Volunteers/nominees read lines spoken by GOBLIN 5, GOBLIN 4, WITCH 7 and GOBLIN 3. You read additional lines spoken by other characters.
- SCENE 3: Read all the lines yourself.
- SCENE 4: Volunteers/nominees read lines spoken by SERVANT 1 and THE QUEEN. You read lines spoken by SERVANT 2.
- SCENE 5: Volunteers/nominees read lines spoken by GOBLIN 1, GOBLIN 9, GOBLIN 5, GOBLIN 4, GOBLIN 7, GOBLIN 3, WITCH 3 and WITCH 7. You read additional lines spoken by other characters.

At the end of each scene, and of the whole play, thank the children for their efforts, including the two groups of GOBLINS and WITCHES. When the play reading has been completed, ask the children to turn to the first page of the script again, and then move quickly on to…

FOCUSED WORD WORK

EXPLORING THE LANGUAGE USED IN THE PLAYSCRIPT

Invite the children to identify words from the text which they have difficulty in understanding. Specify that these must be words which they have never seen or heard before. Write these words on the board. Work through the script quickly, recording all suggestions from the children. Use any remaining time to provide definitions of these words.

This can be achieved in a number of different ways:

- by the children looking the words up in a dictionary, working individually with teacher guidance
- by the children working in small groups, being allocated three or four words per group, and looking them up in a dictionary
- by the teacher providing the definitions of the words on the board
- by the teacher providing the definitions of some of the words on the board, but asking children to discover the others.

The process of defining words can be made more interesting by creating teams and allocating a team point each time that a word is defined correctly.

Ensure that these new words and their definitions are recorded: on paper, in spelling books, or in writing books. Leave any words not defined for further work at a later time, and move on to…

GROUP WORK
SMALL GROUP READINGS OF THE PLAYSCRIPT

Form the children into four groups of seven to nine (preferably of mixed reading ability). Ensure that each child retains his or her playscript. Tell them that you want each group to read scenes from the play, speaking the character lines aloud with the other members of their group. Inform the children that they

will be expected to read all of the lines spoken by the different characters in their allotted scenes, and that this may mean some children reading more than one part. Advise the children to negotiate and distribute the character parts fairly, ensuring that each person in the group reads at least once. Allocate each group a section of the play as follows:

- Group 1: Scene 1.
- Group 2: Scene 2.
- Group 3: Scenes 3 and 4.
- Group 4: Scene 5.

Move from group to group, allocating the scenes and ensuring that parts have been fairly distributed. When you have visited each group, instruct the children to begin their play readings. Move around the room monitoring the readings and assisting where necessary. Allow sufficient time for all readings to be completed. If time remains, ask each group in sequence to read their play section aloud to the others.

Thank the children for their efforts, ask them to stop reading, tell them to turn and face the board again, and move on to…

STORY OUTLINE
WHOLE-CLASS REVIEW AND CONSOLIDATION OF KNOWLEDGE GAINED

Attach the sheet of A3 paper to the board. Write the heading 'A Suitably Happy Ending' on it. Invite the children to recall the story told in the playscript, asking them to suggest sentences which provide a sequential outline of the events. Guide their observations by

asking: *What is happening at the beginning of the play?*

Record their answer on the A3 paper. Follow this by asking: *What is the next important thing that happens?* Continue in this fashion until you have the complete story of the events of the play written in sequential outline form. Take a final moment to confirm with the children that you have recorded all of the important elements of the story. Thank the children for their contributions and retain the sheet for use in the following session.

SESSION 3:
EXPLORING THE STORYLINE

Timing: Spend up to 15 minutes on each activity. The whole session should take no more than 45 minutes.
Resources: A large space (such as the school hall), A3 sheet from the previous session, chairs (optional).
Objectives: To consolidate knowledge of the play text and develop drama skills.

WHO'S SPEAKING?
DEVELOPS LISTENING SKILLS AND STORYLINE SEQUENCING

Ask the children to lie down in a space on the floor and to close their eyes.

Explain that you are going to tap one of them on the shoulder and that, when tapped, that child must begin telling the story of what happens in *A Suitably Happy Ending*. Tell the other children to listen very carefully to both the voice and the section of the story being told. Explain that after a short while you will tap the child again, signalling them to stop speaking.

Then invite the other children to identify the speaker. When correctly identified, select another speaker to continue the story from the point at which the previous speaker concluded.

Again, this speaker should be asked to stop and the other children invited to identify him or her. All children must keep their eyes closed at all times!

The process should be repeated until the whole story of the play has been recalled in this manner. Thank the children for their efforts, instruct them to open their eyes and sit up, and move on to...

SCENE FREEZES
PROVIDES A FOCUS FOR HIGHLIGHTING ELEMENTS OF THE STORY

Ask the children to form groups of five to eight and to find a space to work in. Allocate a scene from the play to each group. (Allocate Scene 4 to a group of six children, with each half creating one freeze – a still and silent picture). Instruct each group to create two freezes which represent what happens in their specified scene.

Advise the children to discuss the events in their scene thoroughly before deciding which elements to represent in their freezes. Allow the children up to 5 minutes to discuss and create their two freezes. View each group's two freezes in sequence until the events of each scene of the play have been represented through frozen images.

Insist on stillness and silence in the freezes and ensure that the observers remain quiet whilst they are operating as the 'audience'. Thank the children for their efforts, ask them to sit in a large circle, and move on to...

A Suitably Happy Ending

MIMING TO NARRATION

DEVELOPS VERBAL SKILLS AND CONSOLIDATES KNOWLEDGE OF PLAY CONTENT

Ask the children to recall the story outline of the play which they created at the end of the previous session. Bring forward the A3 sheet to confirm their recollections. Tell them that they are now going to use this story outline to express the play in narration and mime only.

Advise the children that narration is telling the audience what is happening and mime is movement without words or sounds. Ask the children to form groups of four to six. Tell them that each group will narrate, in their own words, what happens in a particular section of the story and will accompany their narrations with the appropriate mimed actions.

Advise the children that they should divide their group into those who will narrate the events and those who will provide the actions. Inform the children that they can have as many narrators as required. Allocate each group up to three of the sequential outline sentences from those recorded on the sheet.

Ask the children to spend time preparing their narrations and mimes and advise them to make their narratives brief enough to recall in performance. Allow each group up to 8 minutes to devise the narrative and mime for their outline section(s).

Move from group to group, ensuring that children are working productively. When the time limit for preparation and rehearsal has elapsed, ask all of the groups to stop working. Specify the sequential order in which the narrated mimes will be performed. Ask each group to perform their narrated mime(s) in turn.

Insist that the audience remain silent whilst others are performing and invite them to applaud after each narrated mime. Continue until all of the narrated mimes have been performed, and the whole story outline has been told in narration and mime. Thank the children for their efforts and ask them to sit in a circle with you again. End the session with...

CIRCLE

CHILDREN REFLECT ON AND EVALUATE THEIR SKILLS AND KNOWLEDGE

Ask the children whether or not they enjoyed the drama session. Invite opinions and reasons.

● What do they think they have learned and achieved from it?
● What do they feel they have done well? What could they have done better?
● How do they think the activities could help them when they are performing?
● Ask them to confirm what they now know about the story of *A Suitably Happy Ending*.

This information could be used as a basis for future workshop sessions.

12

SESSION 4:
CHARACTERIZATION AND ROLE-PLAY

Timing: Spend up to 20 minutes on each activity. The whole session should take no more than 60 minutes.

Resources: A large space (such as the school hall), cards with character names written on them, whistle, chairs (optional).

Objectives: To explore characters and encourage appropriate use of movement and language for role-play.

CHARACTER MOVEMENT
INTRODUCES CHARACTERIZATION

Ask the children to walk around the room carefully, without bumping into or touching each other. Advise them to listen out for your whistle. After a short time, blow the whistle, call out the name of a type of character often found in fairy stories, such as A Wicked Witch, and tell the children to continue moving around the room in the style and manner of that type of character. (Or a Brave Hero, an Evil Goblin, a Noble King/Queen, a Handsome Prince/Beautiful Princess – the choice is up to you, but all should move around as the same type of character).

Advise the children that they can accompany their movements with sound effects, but should continue to listen carefully for your whistle. Watch them as they move around the room in the style of the character, commenting positively on those children expressing the character type well in their movements.

After a short while, blow the whistle and instruct the children to walk as themselves again. Then blow the whistle again, and ask the children to move around the room in the style and manner of another type of character.

Repeat the process until the children have moved in the manner of at least three different character types. Ask the children to stop walking, thank them for their efforts, instruct them to sit in a circle, and move on to...

CHARACTER MIMES
DEVELOPS CHARACTER MOVEMENT

Gather your prepared cards with a different character name written on each one, such as WITCH 1 (or GOBLIN 1, GOBLIN 2, FATHER, JACK, SERVANT 1, the QUEEN – choose any characters from the play).

Tell the children you are going to ask for volunteers each to choose a card and mime the actions of the character written on the card. Remind the children that mimes are movements without sound. Inform them that each mime will be performed to the rest of the group who will try and guess the character being mimed.

Advise the children that their mime should express the character on the card as effectively as possible. Explain that, once a character has been guessed correctly, then a new volunteer will be chosen to select and mime a different character from the cards. Call each volunteer out of the circle to select their card, to prevent other children from hearing or seeing the character name.

Ask each volunteer to perform their mime in the centre of the circle, or where everyone can see. Thank each child after their character mime. Repeat and continue until all character cards have been mimed.

Praise the children for their efforts, ask them to find a partner and a space to work in, and move quickly on to...

ARGUMENTS

DEVELOPING CHARACTER LANGUAGE

In their pairs, ask the children to label themselves 'A' and 'B'. Tell them to imagine that 'A' is one of the GOBLINS and 'B' is one of the WITCHES. Ask the children to act out a conversation between the two characters, with them arguing about who left the lid off the tube of toothpaste.

Ask the 'B's (playing the WITCHES) to begin the argument by accusing the 'A's of leaving the lid off. Specify that there is to be no physical contact between the two characters! Allow the arguments to continue for a few seconds and then instruct the children to swap roles, so that 'A' now becomes one of the WITCHES and 'B' one of the GOBLINS.

After a few seconds, change the situation so that 'A' now becomes SERVANT 1 and 'B' becomes SERVANT 2. Tell the children to act out the servants arguing with each other about which of them the QUEEN likes best and why.

Again, specify no physical contact. After a few seconds, ask the children to swap roles again (this should involve them swapping viewpoints).

In a third situation, tell the 'A's that they are now JACK and the 'B's that they are JACK'S FATHER. Instruct the children to act out an argument between the two characters, with JACK'S FATHER stating why JACK should be banished and JACK stating why he should be allowed to stay with the family. 'No physical contact' rules still apply. Again, after a few seconds, instruct the children to swap roles.

Allow no preparation time – the arguments should be enacted spontaneously. During each improvised conversation, move around the room commenting positively on the acting and in particular praising those children who are expressing their characters well. (The exercise can be made more lively by asking children to change partners for each different improvisation). When the children have enacted each argument, thank them for their efforts and ask them to sit in a circle again. End with...

CIRCLE

CHILDREN REFLECT ON AND EVALUATE THEIR SKILLS AND KNOWLEDGE

Ask the children whether or not they enjoyed the drama session. Invite them to give their opinions and reasons.

- What do they think they have learned and achieved from it?
- What do they feel they have done well? What could they have done better?
- How do they think the activities could help then when they are performing?
- What have they learned about the characters in *A Suitably Happy Ending*?

This information could be used as a basis for future workshop sessions.

SESSION 5:
CONSOLIDATING PERFORMANCE SKILLS

Timing: Spend up to 20 minutes on each activity. The whole session should take no more than 60 minutes.

Resources: A large space (such as the school hall), character cards (from Session 4), sequential story outline (from Session 2), copies of the playscript, sheet of A3 paper and pen (optional).

Objectives: To consolidate knowledge of the play, to develop performance skills.

CHARACTER IMPROVISATIONS
DEVELOPS CREATIVE SKILLS

Ask the children to form groups of five to seven. Ask each group to select a character card (selection should be made without seeing what is written on the cards).

When each group has chosen a character card, explain that you want them to devise a short, original play based around that particular character, and that you want them to improvise how their character would react in different situations. Advise the children that their improvisations must be original.

Explain that each group will perform their short play to the others.

Allow each group up to 8 minutes to plan and rehearse their play. After this time, ask each group in turn to show their improvisations. Ensure that those

observing as the audience are silent whilst others are performing, and invite them to applaud after each improvisation has been shown. Thank all of the children for their work, praise their efforts, and move on to...

STORYLINE IMPROVISATION
CONSOLIDATES TEXT KNOWLEDGE AND DEVELOPS PERFORMANCE SKILLS

Ask the children to sit down where they are. Tell them that you want them to work in their groups to perform different sections of *A Suitably Happy Ending*. Explain that they will use actions and dialogue (conversation and/or narration) to bring their section of the story to life in their own words. These improvisations of the different sections will then be acted out in turn to make up a performance of the whole play.

Using the story outline sheet from Session 2, allocate each group up to three of the sequential sentences. Ensure that all of the children are clear about which sentences have been allocated to their group and what they have to do.

Allow the children up to 5 minutes to plan and rehearse their storyline improvisations. Now ask each group to show their performances in sequence to the class. Tell the children acting as the audience to remain silent whilst others are performing, and invite them to applaud after each group's improvisations.

Thank all of the children for their work, and praise their efforts. Move quickly on to...

SCRIPT EXTRACTS

REINTRODUCES THE SCRIPT AND PREPARES CHILDREN FOR PERFORMANCE

Tell the children that you are going to ask them to perform sections of the script aloud to each other in groups. Their performances can either be simple readings or include actions as well. Distribute copies of the script, retaining one for yourself.

Put the children into groups (ideally of mixed reading ability) and allocate script extracts for performance. Tell the children that some of them may have to speak the lines for more than one character. You could use the following extracts, or others of your choice:

- Ten to twelve children – Scenes 1 and 2.
- Seven children – Scene 3.
- Three children – Scene 4.
- Ten to twelve children – Scene 5.

Performances can be static or moved; but the children should be encouraged to use vocal and facial expression. Allow the children up to 8 minutes to read and rehearse their script extracts. Move from group to group, ensuring that parts have been distributed fairly and that all children are working productively.

When the rehearsal time has elapsed, ask the groups to perform their script extracts in sequence. Insist on silence from the audience whilst others are performing, and invite observers to applaud the actors after each performance. When all of the groups have performed their extracts, thank the children and praise their efforts. Ask them to sit in a circle again, and end the session with…

CIRCLE

CHILDREN REFLECT ON AND EVALUATE THEIR SKILLS AND KNOWLEDGE

Ask the children whether or not they enjoyed the drama session. Invite opinions and reasons.

- Which aspects did they enjoy the most and the least? Why?
- What do they think they have learned or achieved from the session?
- What do they feel is the most important skill they have learned?
- What do they feel they have done well? What could they have done better?
- How do they feel about their performances?
- What would they change if they had the chance to perform again?
- What do they think is the most important thing to remember when performing in front of an audience?

Acknowledge all responses. Thank the children for their hard work, and praise their efforts. If you wish, record their answers on an A3 sheet of paper to provide a visual prompt during rehearsals of the play.

A Suitably Happy Ending

CAST LIST

Narrator(s)
(this role can be shared amongst an additional 2 to 3 children)

Goblin 1
Goblin 2
Goblin 3
Goblin 4
Goblin 5
Goblin 6
Goblin 7
Goblin 8
Goblin 9
Witch 1
Witch 2
Witch 3
Witch 4

Witch 5
Witch 6
Witch 7
Mother
Jack
Father
Brother
Sister 1
Sister 2
Servant 1
Servant 2
The Queen

26 characters
(and the option of an additional 3 Narrators = 29)

Children who prefer non-speaking roles can be included as additional Witches and Goblins. Their confidence can be built by encouraging them to join in with the 'choral' lines, or they can be allowed to remain silent and act only with their faces and bodies.

SCENES

1 The village street.
2 Outside the Castle on the Hill.
3 Jack's home.
4 The Queen's palace.
5 In the Large and Spooky Forest.

Photocopiable

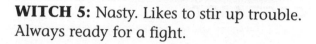

CHARACTER OUTLINES

NARRATOR: Tells the audience what's happening in the story. Starts and ends the play.

GOBLIN 1: Leader of the Goblins. Very bossy and quite nasty.

GOBLIN 2: Nervous and panics easily. Loyal to Goblin 1.

GOBLIN 3: Unpleasant and sarcastic to others.

GOBLIN 4: Nasty and rude to outsiders but loyal to the Goblins.

GOBLIN 5: Nasty and a bit of a bully.

GOBLIN 6: The happiest Goblin. Not very bright but very cheerful.

GOBLIN 7: A Goblin with leadership qualities. Strong and bossy.

GOBLIN 8: Nervous. Doesn't like arguments. Doesn't really like being a nasty Goblin.

GOBLIN 9: Nasty to the Witches. Can be considerate. Very loyal to the Goblins.

WITCH 1: Leader of the Witches. Very unpleasant.

WITCH 2: Loyal to the Witches. Can be very sarcastic and rude.

WITCH 3: Likes a fight. Always ready to attack others.

WITCH 4: Quiet. Very loyal to Witch 1. Always agrees with the other Witches.

WITCH 5: Nasty. Likes to stir up trouble. Always ready for a fight.

WITCH 6: Very loyal to the Witches. Absolutely hates Goblins.

WITCH 7: Not very bright, but very loyal and always willing to support the other Witches.

MOTHER: Worries about what other people think of her. Over-reacts to every situation.

JACK: The hero. Kind and always tries his best. Pleasant to others but not always treated well.

FATHER: Bad tempered. Supports Mother. Also worries about what other people think.

BROTHER: An unpleasant little show-off. Self-centred.

SISTER 1: An even more unpleasant little show-off. Loyal to Mother and Father.

SISTER 2: Bored with everything. Goes her own way. Doesn't care about others.

SERVANT 1: Not very bright. Panics about everything. Loyal to the Queen.

SERVANT 2: Not very bright, either. Calmer than Servant 1. Loyal to the Queen.

THE QUEEN: Pleasant but slightly dim. Kind to others. A bit bored with being Queen.

Photocopiable

SCENE 1: **The village street**

The NARRATOR enters.

NARRATOR: Once upon a time, a long, long time ago, the goblins and the witches lived together happily as friends. There was never a cross word between them and they never used their magic powers against each other.

GOBLINS 1, 3, 4, 5, 6, 7, 8 and 9 and ALL WITCHES enter. The two groups greet each other with exaggerated politeness.

GOBLIN 1: *(politely)* Good morning, Witch, and how are you today?

WITCH 1: I'm very well thank you, Goblin. Isn't it a lovely morning? And how are you?

GOBLIN 1: I'm feeling just fine, thank you. So nice of you to ask.

GOBLIN 2 enters hurriedly, in great distress.

GOBLIN 2: *(frightened)* Quick, quick, there's a huge dragon just outside the village and it's heading this way! It's in a really bad mood, too!

GOBLIN 3: Right! We'll sort this out, don't you fear. *(To the other GOBLINS)* Come on, Goblins, let's see to that dragon.

ALL OTHER GOBLINS: *(in unison)* Right!

The GOBLINS move as if to exit.

WITCH 2: *(stopping them politely)* No, no, we couldn't possibly let you put yourselves in danger. Let us witches deal with this for you. *(To the other WITCHES)* Come on you lot!

ALL OTHER WITCHES: *(in unison)* Right!

The WITCHES move as if to exit.

ALL GOBLINS: *(in unison – stopping the WITCHES)* No!

ALL WITCHES: *(in unison)* We insist!

The GOBLINS all pause, then say…

ALL GOBLINS: *(in unison)* Oh, all right then. Thank you SO much.

All GOBLINS exit.
All WITCHES exit in a different direction – towards the dragon
(exiting where GOBLIN 2 entered).
The NARRATOR enters.

NARRATOR: Life went on like that for hundreds of years. The Goblins and Witches lived together in peaceful harmony – as Goblins and Witches so rarely do – until one awful morning when, for some strange and unexplainable reason, everything suddenly started to go horribly wrong…

The NARRATOR exits. WITCH 5 enters.

WITCH 5: Goblin! Come here this minute! *(GOBLIN 7 enters)* You've left the top off the toothpaste tube again!

GOBLIN 7: No I haven't, it wasn't me. Why not ask one of your Witches?

WITCH 5: THEY wouldn't do it. If it wasn't you then it must have been one of the other Goblins. *(Shouts loudly towards offstage)* Witches!

ALL WITCHES enter.

GOBLIN 7: I'm telling you it WASN'T a Goblin. We always tidy up after ourselves. *(Shouts loudly towards offstage in a different direction)* Goblins!

ALL GOBLINS enter.

Photocopiable

WITCH 5: *(to the other WITCHES)* One of these untidy Goblins has left the top off the toothpaste again. I'm fed up with their inconsiderate behaviour – they have no thought for anyone else living here.

GOBLIN 7: *(to the other GOBLINS)* This Witch automatically assumes that it was one of us! Is this fair?

ALL OTHER GOBLINS: *(in unison)* No!

GOBLIN 7: Is this right?

ALL OTHER GOBLINS: *(in unison)* No!

GOBLIN 7: Are we going to stand for it?! Are we going to take it lying down?!

ALL OTHER GOBLINS: *(in unison, standing upright)* No! *(Lying down)* No! *(Standing again)* No! No! No!

WITCH 1: As leader of the Witches, I have a duty to my people. If you will not admit your mistake and refuse to apologize, then there is only one thing for it... we will have to fight for our honour.

GOBLIN 1: As leader of the Goblins, I have a duty to my people. We refuse to be blamed for something we didn't do and will NOT apologize. We, too, will fight for our honour.

GOBLIN 8: *(timidly)* Er... excuse me... Couldn't we just sit down and discuss this like sensible people instead of...?

ALL WITCHES & OTHER GOBLINS: *(in unison, to GOBLIN 8)* Shut up!!

GOBLIN 8: *(offended)* All right, all right, there's no need to shout.

WITCH 1: Meet you outside the Castle on the Hill at 7 o'clock. And don't be late.

GOBLIN 1: Late? Huh! Just you try and stop us.

WITCH 1: And don't bring dopey, there. *(Points to Goblin 8.)*

GOBLIN 8: *(protesting)* I'm not a dwarf, I'm a Goblin! My name's...

ALL WITCHES: Shut up!

GOBLIN 8: *(even more offended)* Well, really! How rude.

ALL WITCHES and GOBLINS exit in different directions, talking amongst themselves and preparing for battle.
The NARRATOR enters.

NARRATOR: And, so, from this silly little misunderstanding erupted one of the most vicious battles in fairy tale history. The Witches had magic powers but the Goblins could be REALLY nasty! Many Goblins and Witches suffered that night, but the casualties were greater on the Witches' side. The battle was just too horrible to show you but it's enough for you to know that a sadly reduced group of Goblins were eventually victorious and that the remaining Witches were stripped of their magic powers and driven out of the village to languish in shame in the Large and Spooky Forest.

The NARRATOR exits.

SCENE 2: **Outside the Castle on the Hill**

GOBLINS 1, 3, 4, 5, 6, 7 and 9 enter.
WITCHES 1, 3, 6 and 7 enter.
It is after the battle. They all have various wounds and everyone
looks tired and battle-weary.

GOBLIN 9: *(To the WITCHES, threateningly)* ...and don't you come back again! Or else!

ALL OTHER GOBLINS: Yeah!!

GOBLIN 5: And take your stupid toothpaste tube with you! *(Throws a tube of toothpaste at the Witches.)*

ALL OTHER GOBLINS: *(laughing)* Yeah!!

GOBLIN 3: Oh, look! No lid – wonder where that can be?

All GOBLINS laugh and snigger.

GOBLIN 4: Must have been eaten by the dragon.

The GOBLINS all laugh again.

WITCH 6: You nasty little Goblins. I do HATE people who make fun of others when they're down. It's just spiteful.

WITCH 7: Yeah. You just wait. We might be gone but we've not forgotten. We'll get you back one day.

ALL OTHER WITCHES: *(uncertainly)* Yeah! Just you wait.

WITCH 1: *(in 'Terminator' style – like Arnold Schwarzenegger)* I'll be back.

ALL WITCHES exit.
ALL GOBLINS exit, laughing, in a different direction.
The NARRATOR enters.

NARRATOR: And, so, the Witches left and the Goblins lived a wonderful life alone in the village. They ate all the food, drank all the drink and spent all the Witches' gold – which was really very naughty indeed. I think they needed a good telling-off personally, especially stealing someone else's money, I mean…

GOBLIN 3:   *(shouting from offstage)* Get on with it!

NARRATOR: All, right, all right! Anyway, the Goblins lived the high life whilst the Witches were gone. Meanwhile, on the other side of the Large and Spooky Forest which surrounded the village, another part of the story was unfolding…

The NARRATOR exits.

Photocopiable

SCENE 3: **Jack's home**

MOTHER, FATHER, BROTHER, SISTER 1 and SISTER 2 enter with two chairs which they position facing the audience.

MOTHER: *(looking towards offstage)* Isn't it time that Jack was home with his SATs results?

JACK enters from a different direction.

JACK: *(calling out as he enters)* Mother! I'm home with my SATs results! *(He waves the envelope in the air.)*

FATHER: *(snatches the envelope from JACK)* Let me see!

MOTHER: *(snatches the envelope from FATHER)* Let me see!

BROTHER: *(snatches the envelope from MOTHER)* Let me see!

SISTER 1: *(snatches the envelope from BROTHER)* Let me see!

SISTER 2: *(takes the envelope from SISTER 1 and, bored, passes it to MOTHER)* I'm not interested.

MOTHER opens the envelope, reads the report inside and faints, collapsing on the floor.

FATHER: Now look what you've gone and done, you've made your poor mother faint. *(To MOTHER)* Are they that good?

FATHER takes the report from MOTHER's hands, reads the results and nearly faints but manages to stagger and collapse onto a chair instead.

JACK: *(hopeful)* Are they good, Father? Have I done well?

FATHER: *(angry)* Good? Good?! These are the worst SATs results we've ever had in this house, my boy!

JACK: Oh. *(Pause)* Oh dear.

Photocopiable

A Suitably Happy Ending

FATHER: Don't you "Oh dear" me! I'll give you "Oh dear"! I'll "Oh dear" you so hard you won't be able to sit down for weeks! No one has ever achieved such bad results in our family before.

MOTHER: *(still lying on the floor; wails)* He's brought disgrace on our family!

BROTHER: *(showing off)* I got Level 5 in MY SATs results.

SISTER 1: *(showing off even more)* I got Level 6 in MY SATs results.

SISTER 2: *(still very bored)* I don't really care. I'm still not interested.

MOTHER: *(staggering to her feet and collapsing onto a chair)* You can't stay here! What will people think? We don't want them to know that you belong to this family! *(Wailing)* Oh! The shame of it! The shame of it!

JACK: But I tried my best, isn't that all anyone can do?

FATHER: *(angry)* Don't talk nonsense, boy! You must leave this house immediately – and don't come back!

SISTER 1: *(shocked)* Oh no!

BROTHER: *(even more shocked)* Oh no!

SISTER 2: *(excited)* Great! Can I have his bedroom?

JACK: *(upset)* But where will I go?

FATHER: *(pointing offstage, towards the 'forest')* You must go into the Large and Spooky Forest. Keep well away from us, we don't want to know you any more.

JACK: *(terrified)* Oh no! Not the Large and Spooky Forest! It's so large and spooky!

MOTHER: Leave now and never darken our door again. *(Wailing again)* Oh, how will I be able to hold my head up at the PTA meetings now?

JACK: *(pleading)* Please, Mother, please Father, can't I stay? I'll do better next time.

ALL THE FAMILY: *(pointing to the exit and in unison)* Go!!

SISTER 2:   *(waving cheerfully)* Byeee!

JACK exits towards the 'Large and Spooky Forest'.
MOTHER, FATHER, BROTHER, SISTER 1 and SISTER 2 exit in a
different direction, taking the chairs off with them.
The NARRATOR enters.

NARRATOR: And so, poor Jack was thrown out of his home with no food and no money and, to make things worse – if they could possibly be worse – he was cast out into the Large and Spooky Forest, a place where few people dared to go. *(Pause)* Meanwhile the Queen of Jack's village was having her usual problems at the palace...

The NARRATOR exits.

SCENE 4: **The Queen's palace**

SERVANT 1 rushes on in a panic. SERVANT 2 enters slowly behind.

SERVANT 1: *(running around the stage frantically)* Her Majesty is coming!

SERVANT 2: *(standing and watching SERVANT 1 with puzzled amusement)* Her Majesty is coming? Why are you running around like that? What's all the panic? How many times do I have to tell you that she's a NICE Queen?!

SERVANT 1: *(still running around)* I HAVE to run around in a panic like this, it's a servant's job! *(Shouting)* HER MAJESTY IS COMING! HER MAJESTY IS COMING! MAKE WAY FOR HER MAJESTY!!

SERVANT 2: *(to SERVANT 1)* Will you stop shouting and running around like that? You're giving me a really bad headache, and if I'm not careful it could turn into a very nasty migraine.

The QUEEN enters. She is wearing a pair of glasses. SERVANT 2 bows to her.

SERVANT 1: *(bowing to the QUEEN)* Bow low for Her Majesty.

SERVANT 2: *(straightens up)* What?

SERVANT 1: *(pushing Servant 2 into bowing position again)* Bow low for Her Majesty!

SERVANT 2: *(in bowing position)* I WAS bowing until... Oh, never mind.

Both SERVANTS remain in a bowing position.

SERVANT 1: Welcome, Your Majesty, is there anything we can do to be of service to Your Majesty? Can we cook you anything? Clean your clothes? Polish your silver? Anything at all?

Photocopiable

SERVANT 2: *(to SERVANT 1)* Oh, do stop grovelling, it's embarrassing and pathetic.

QUEEN: *(also bending over into a bowing position to talk to them)* No, thank you, it's very nice of you to offer but everything's been seen to, I've sorted most of it out myself.

SERVANT 1: *(still bowing)* Would Your Majesty like us to read you a story or…

SERVANT 2: *(still bowing)* …Oh, for heaven's sake!

They are ALL still bowing.

QUEEN: No thank you. *(Pause)* Um, why are we all bending over like this?

SERVANT 1: We're bowing to you, Your Majesty. You haven't told us to "arise" yet.

QUEEN: *(straightening up)* Oh, I see! Right! Arise then, please.

SERVANT 1 and SERVANT 2 straighten up. SERVANT 2 rubs his back as if in pain.

QUEEN: I think I'll take a little walk into the Large and Spooky Forest. I seem to have lost my glasses again and think I might have left them there when I went in there for that picnic. See you later.

The QUEEN exits towards the Large and Spooky Forest.

SERVANT 2: *(to SERVANT 1)* Do you think we should have told her that she was wearing them?

SERVANT 1: No, no! We're just servants. It's not in our job description to tell the Queen things like that.

SERVANT 2: Oh, I just thought it might make her feel less of an idiot when she realizes, that's all.

Photocopiable

A Suitably Happy Ending

SERVANT 1: It's not our job to make Her Majesty feel less of an idiot. She is entitled to feel how she likes.

SERVANT 2: Oh, righto. *(Pause)* Fancy a game of chess?

SERVANT 1: All right, but only if you let me keep score this time.

SERVANT 2: Well just you make sure that you do the adding up and taking away properly then!

SERVANT 1 and SERVANT 2 exit, chatting to each other.

SCENE 5: **The Large and Spooky Forest**

The NARRATOR enters. JACK enters, looking very afraid and walking slowly and cautiously, looking around him in fear.

NARRATOR: In the Large and Spooky Forest, poor Jack was wandering around cold, hungry and very, very frightened. He still hadn't quite got over his family's reaction to his SATs results and was beginning to wonder just how long he'd be able to survive.

The NARRATOR exits.

JACK: *(looking down)* Oh! Ants! Thank goodness! My first proper meal since being cast out into the Large and Spooky Forest.

JACK crouches down by the 'anthill'. GOBLINS 1, 3, 4, 5, 6, 7 and 9 enter and creep up behind him.

ALL GOBLINS: *(in unison)* Who are you and what are you doing in our forest?

JACK jumps violently and stands up.

JACK: *(nervously)* What! Who said that?! *(Looking down, unhappily)* Oh no! You've made me stand on my dinner.

Photocopiable

30

GOBLIN 1: *(nastily)* I am the leader of the Goblins and this is OUR forest. What are you doing here?

JACK: I'm Jack and I've been cast out by my family. I'm cold and hungry. Do you have anything to eat?

GOBLIN 1: *(thoughtfully)* We might have. Just a minute, please, we've got to have a meeting.

GOBLIN 6: *(excited)* A meeting! A meeting! We've got to have a meeting!

ALL of the GOBLINS gather together in a huddle away from JACK and speak towards the audience.

GOBLIN 1: If we give him food, we could use it to bribe him and take him back to our village.

GOBLIN 6: Yeah! *(Pause, and then puzzled)* Why would we want to do that then?

GOBLIN 1: *(sighs)* So that we can make him our slave and keep him working for us for ever.

GOBLIN 9: Won't his parents be worried about him?

GOBLIN 1: You heard him, he's been cast out by his family, THEY won't even be bothered if he never comes home.

GOBLIN 5: *(thinking aloud)* I'd like a slave, he could fetch my 'Beano' for me from the corner shop.

GOBLIN 4: Yeah! And he could do the washing up and save my hands from getting all wrinkled and sore.

GOBLIN 1: *(looking at the other GOBLINS)* Is that settled, then? We offer him food as a bribe to come back with us?

ALL OTHER GOBLINS: *(in unison. Looking at each other and then back to GOBLIN 1)* Yeah!

Photocopiable

A Suitably Happy Ending

The huddle breaks up and the GOBLINS move back to JACK who has been watching with puzzlement.

GOBLIN 1:   We CAN give you food...

JACK: *(jumps excitedly)* Yippeee!

GOBLIN 7:   ...but on one condition...

JACK: *(disappointedly)* Oh.

GOBLIN 3:   You must come back with us and work for us.

JACK: *(hopefully)* Paid work?

GOBLIN 3:   No, it's a voluntary position, but you will get lots of experience.

JACK: I'm so hungry I'd agree to anything right now.

GOBLIN 5:   Is that a "yes"?

JACK: Yes! Yes! Please, just give me the food.

The QUEEN enters. She is searching the ground as she walks.

QUEEN: Has anybody seen my glasses? I'm sure I left them here somewhere. *(To JACK)* Who are you? *(Pointing to the GOBLINS)* And who are they?

JACK: You're wearing your glasses, Your Majesty. I'm Jack and I've been cast out by my family. These are Goblins who are going to let me work for them in return for some food – which I really could do with right now.

QUEEN: Goblins, eh? I've heard some very bad things about Goblins. I wouldn't trust them if I were you.

GOBLIN 7:   No, no, we're lovely people. Just misunderstood.

Photocopiable

Suddenly WITCHES 1, 3, 6 and 7 enter.

GOBLIN 9: *(Noticing the WITCHES)* Oh no! Witches! How did they get in here? Why haven't they vanished forever?

The QUEEN takes JACK to one side and protects him.

WITCH 1: *(To the GOBLINS, nastily)* You can never get rid of a witch for long – you silly Goblins. I told you I'd be back and here I am!

WITCH 3: The Wizard of the deep, dark cave helped us to restore our powers and we have come to seek our revenge!

GOBLIN 1: Oh, crickey! *(Worried)* Look, we're really sorry about the misunderstanding over the toothpaste. Can't we just forget all about it and just be friends? I'm sure we can all have a really good laugh about it later. *(Laughs nervously.)*

The WITCHES move menacingly towards the GOBLINS throughout the following.
The GOBLINS continue to back off slowly and nervously.
Eventually both WITCHES and GOBLINS end up offstage in the wings.

WITCH 1: Laugh? Laugh! You Goblins killed some of my best witches. I don't think that's very funny at all.

GOBLIN 4: Oh, Oh. We're in real trouble now.

WITCH 6: *(In 'Terminator' style again)* Hasta la vista, Goblins!

WITCH 7: Yeah! Hand me the pizza!!

The WITCHES and GOBLINS are now both offstage.
Horrible battle noises, screams and gurgles can be heard as the two groups fight with each other again.
The QUEEN and JACK react on stage to the sounds coming from offstage and are both quite afraid.
Eventually the WITCHES re-enter. WITCH 1 dusts imaginary dirt from her palms.
The WITCHES congratulate each other on winning the battle.

Photocopiable

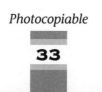

33

WITCH 1:   Well, that's got rid of those nasty little Goblins for good!

JACK: Oh no, poor Goblins!

The WITCHES all turn and suddenly notice the QUEEN and JACK for the first time.

JACK: Oh dear, I don't think I should have said that.

WITCH 3:   *(looking nastily at JACK and the QUEEN)* What have we here? Witnesses! They must be eliminated.

They move menacingly towards JACK and the QUEEN.

QUEEN: *(holding up her hands to stop the WITCHES)* Stop witches! I, too have magic powers which I received from my Fairy Godmother when I was just a baby. Now, let me see if I can remember the rhyme.

JACK: Well, think quickly, for goodness sake!

QUEEN: *(thinking)* Umm. *(Remembering suddenly)* Oh, yes! *(Directing her outstretched arms towards the WITCHES)* "Wood you are and wood you'll be, turned forever into a tree!"

The WITCHES all freeze in 'tree' shapes and remain frozen to the end of the play.

JACK: Well done! I was really impressed with that! Nice bit of magic. Could you possibly find me a spell to get me some food before I pass out right here in front of you?

QUEEN: I can do better than that. You can come back to my castle with me and I'll give you all the food you could wish for. You can stay as long as you like as well. I'm really fed up with those two servants of mine – they think I'M stupid but I know stupid when I see it and I see it when I look at them. It'll be nice to have some intelligent company for a change.

JACK: Well you won't get that from me, I failed my SATs.

Photocopiable

QUEEN: Oh, don't worry about that, so did I, and look at me!

The QUEEN and JACK exit, chatting happily to each other.
The NARRATOR enters.

NARRATOR: And so the Witches and the Goblins finally managed to destroy each other. Jack stayed with the Queen and got excellent grades in his next SATs results. The Servants and the Queen really enjoyed having an extra person around the castle. Jack's family were ignored by all the other families – word had already got out about his results so they needn't have banished him after all. They did come to the castle to see him, but he refused to speak to them. And the moral of this tale? Well, there isn't one really but I suppose it just shows how dangerous it is to argue about leaving the lid off the toothpaste!

THE END

PRODUCTION SUPPORT

A Suitably Happy Ending

AUDITIONS AND CASTING

The easiest way to begin the audition process is to read the play through with the children two or three times. The initial reading should be used simply to familiarize the children with the material; allocate speeches reading in sequence around the circle. In the second read-through, let the children volunteer to read specific character parts; in the third, nominate specific children to read certain character parts. During the second and third readings, encourage the children to think about using vocal expression, following the stage directions and picking up their cues quickly. Write yourself notes about how the children perform when reading specific roles. At any read-through, you must give every child a chance to read something.

It is important to make a concerted effort to allow less confident readers a chance to read, encouraging others in the group to show patience and consideration when listening. Plays always help poor readers to develop their language skills, and their enthusiasm for performance often leads to a great deal of work away from the rehearsals to ensure that they know their lines. A poor reader does not necessarily make a poor actor.

There are several alternative methods of casting your play and the process can be as formal or informal as you wish.

FORMAL AUDITIONS
These can be held by selecting specific speeches or scenes from the play and asking the children to learn or recite them, or read them through, in various group combinations. The disadvantages of this method are that it takes an inordinate amount of time to plan and execute, and that it makes children very tense and often unable to perform well – especially if their memory skills are not strong. (Even if they are reading the text, a successful audition will depend on their being very familiar with it.)

CHILDREN CHOOSING THEIR OWN ROLES
Another option is to ask the children to write their first and second role choices, confidentially, on pieces of paper. Ask them to try and make sure the spelling is correct and to add their names and surnames on the slips of paper. Some children will only have one choice of role, others will all go for the same first choice and there will be some children who 'don't care' what role they are given.

Gather all the pieces of paper together and, in a quiet place at another time, sit down and work out who wants what and which role combinations would work. Try to be as fair as possible, both to the children and to the play. Children are often aware of their 'failings' as actors and usually accept that others have stronger performance skills, but this doesn't prevent many children from feeling acute disappointment if they fail to secure the role they are desperate for.

When allocating roles after using this method, sit the children in a circle and read from the bottom of the cast list upwards, giving the name of the character first and then the name of the child who has been

given that part. Sometimes a little of what is known as 'director speak' (see below) may be useful in trying to convince upset children that they are more suited to smaller 'character roles' than to a main part. After each part has been given out, allow the children up to 5 minutes to discuss the casting and to accept and compare roles.

DRAWING NAMES OUT OF A HAT

Another method which is fairer, but more risky for your play, is to ask the children to put their names into a hat and to draw a name for each character. Children have mixed feelings about this process: there is always the possibility that their name will be drawn for the character they want to play, but they know that this is not very likely. Also, less confident children occasionally end up with large roles which they really don't feel happy or comfortable with performing.

CHOOSING ACTORS YOURSELF

The final option is simply to allocate the roles yourself, choosing children that you know are able and confident. This can upset a number of other children who are rarely given the opportunity to perform, though, and removes any sense of the children being involved in the casting process at all.

After a number of years and a number of arguments, floods of tears and several very unhappy children, I have reached the conclusion that the second method – children choosing their own roles – is the fairest and surest. It gives children a chance to specify which roles they would like to perform, and gives you the opportunity to make the final decision in a considered manner. It always surprises me which parts children choose to go for, and which appear to be the most popular! Sometimes children who appear confident

– and who might have otherwise been given a major role – select small parts; likewise, children who appear less confident select major roles.

I feel very strongly that children's enthusiasm for playing their roles will result in an easier rehearsal process, an eagerness to learn lines and a willingness to throw themselves into the role whole-heartedly. I have been justified in this belief over and over again when 'risking' a major part on a child who may not have been given a chance to shine had I used a different casting method.

Whichever casting method you choose, you should now ask the children to sit in a circle again, arranging them according to character or family groups. Then read through the play one more time to get the feel of how it sounds with the roles established.

Finally, tell the children that each person in the cast is as important as the next: without any one character, you don't have a full team and, therefore, a complete play. They won't believe you – they've already spent time counting the number of lines they have to say – but it *is* true and needs to be expressed!

DIRECTOR SPEAK

Whatever decisions you make about casting, and however fair you try to be, there will be children who are upset when the parts are distributed. Many children feel that they never have the opportunity to show what they can do; some can build up quite a strong resentment against others who always seem to get the main roles; and quieter children can feel a sense of failure at not having pushed themselves forward yet again.

These feelings need to be dealt with as sensitively and as quickly as possible, away from the main group. In these situations you must employ what is known as 'director speak', in an attempt to pacify, boost and reassure the children. This consists of using a variety of statements aimed to placate, such as:

- *I know you're upset about not getting the part you wanted, but I really needed a good actor for the part you've been given to encourage all of the others to perform well in that scene.*
- *I understand that you wanted a main part, but you read this part so well that I just had to give it to you.*
- *I appreciate that you're disappointed, but I wanted to give you the chance to try something different this time, to show me what you could do.*
- *I know that you're unhappy, but can you understand that I have to be fair to everyone and give others a chance to try a bigger part sometimes?*

And others of a similar nature. The children will probably recognize that you are trying to pacify them, but what is important about using 'director speak' is that you are hearing and acknowledging their feelings of unhappiness and that they have had the opportunity to express them.

Whatever you say isn't going to make a lot of difference for some children; in these cases, they need to be given the direct choice of either playing the part they have been given or not being in the play at all – however cruel it may seem. Most children will choose the former. Any child opting out of the play should be occupied with other tasks, such as painting scenery, prompting, or making props and costumes. They will often regret their decision to pull out and, if possible, should be given the chance to join in again.

The main aspect of the production of a play which is likely to anger and upset children is the part allocation. Therefore if, when using 'director speak'

on a previous occasion you promised someone a bigger part next time, you must keep your promise! Also, if you have stated that 'everyone needs to be given a chance' then don't under any circumstances allocate the main roles to the same children as were chosen last time.

I use 'director speak' all the time, and try to use it in a way that is reasonable, fair and understanding. Used in that way, it works.

STRUCTURING REHEARSALS

When faced with directing a play, it is sometimes difficult to know what to tackle first. You have a large group of children awaiting your instructions, a limited amount of access to the school hall and very little time! Good pre-rehearsal planning and preparation is, therefore, essential. The following timetable has always worked for me and it might be suitable for you, too.

PREPARATION

Immediately after casting, spend an hour or two resolving practicalities: what sort of stage the play will be performed on, how many entrances and exits it will have and where these will be (plus consideration of what imaginary setting lies beyond them if relevant); where the children will go when not on stage, exactly how and where each character enters and exits, what scenery, furniture and props you will have, if any, and where these will be positioned on the stage; whether any characters will enter from other parts of the auditorium and, if so, how.

All of these points need to be clearly defined to your own satisfaction before starting rehearsals.

A Suitably Happy Ending

REHEARSALS 1 TO 3

These should be used to complete what is known as 'blocking' – simply specifying the movements of children on, off and around the stage. Explain your staging ideas to the cast, marking out the stage area and exits using chairs. Tell them what furniture and scenery will be on stage and use chairs or other equipment to represent this as well. Take time to ensure that all of the children in the cast are familiar with the setting, acting arena and their movements before continuing. They'll be desperate to get on with the 'acting', but it is essential that they understand the space they are working in and know their moves, before they try to go any further. It is impossible to teach children to act *and* give them instructions about where to enter and exit at the same time!

REHEARSALS 4 TO 8

Break the play down into small sections and rehearse these individually. Don't try to work through the whole play at a single rehearsal at this point. Start from the beginning and work through a maximum of three scenes. Rehearse the same section a number of times until you feel that familiarity is beginning to reduce interest; then move on to the next section.

Continue the next rehearsal from where you left off last time – never repeat the previous section and then move on, or the result will be one or two sections that are absolutely brilliant and a number that are completely under-rehearsed. (I speak from experience!) This will mean that some children are unoccupied for some of the rehearsals. Set them learning their lines in pairs; watching the play and making notes, giving you feedback about how it looks; making props; designing posters and programmes, and so on. Insist that they remain aware of what is

going on – they could be called to rehearsal at any time!

Carry on rehearsing the play in small sections until you have completed the whole script. Make notes as you go along of any potential difficulties; any scenes or characters which you feel will need extra rehearsing; and any ideas that you have for scenery, props, costumes or effects.

REHEARSALS 9 TO 11

Rehearse the complete play at each rehearsal. Use these rehearsals to concentrate on scenes or sections which need extra attention. Try to get through the whole play at least once during each rehearsal period, but don't panic if you fail to do so. Again, never go back over sections; always start the next rehearsal from the point at which you finished during the last one.

REHEARSALS 12 TO 14

These should be used for complete run-throughs – a technical rehearsal to go over any lights, sound effects, props or music that you might be including; and two dress rehearsals complete with costumes and make-up. Spend 10 minutes at the beginning of the final dress rehearsal to work out and practise your 'curtain call', then run through the play completely without stopping. Final rehearsals are always a nightmare – the children are stressed and excited, you're stressed and beginning to panic and everyone seems to be snapping at each other! Try to keep the children occupied at all times; plan what you want to achieve in the rehearsals and try to stick to your plan.

I appreciate that this is the rehearsal structure for the 'ideal world', and it doesn't take into account those little things sent to try us: children being absent, falling out, not learning their lines or forgetting everything they learned at the last rehearsal; the props and costumes failing to materialize, and so on, but those stresses are what give us the sense of achievement when the play finally goes on – and it *does* always go on, despite the horrendous feeling that it will fail. The old saying 'It'll be all right on the night' usually applies!

STAGING AND SCENERY

A Suitably Happy Ending can be very simple to stage. It was first performed on a proscenium arch stage – a square, raised stage which resembles a box, with structured spaces at the side for 'wings' and full curtains (see the illustration below). There was no set at all, the stage was completely bare, and the characters simply walked on from the wings at the side of the stage to make their entrances, and exited in the same manner. The only scene with any furniture was Scene 3, and Jack's family brought on and removed the chairs they used for this. The drawback of working with a bare stage is that the children need to work harder in their acting to establish settings and create atmospheres.

If you want to be more adventurous and use scenery, there are a number of options open to you:

● If your children are performing on a proscenium arch stage, the solid back wall (known as the cyclorama, or cyc) can be decorated with fixed scenery which will be appropriate for all of the scenes in the play. This could consist of a 'brick wall' pattern, or trees and flowers. Alternatively, the 'general theme' idea can be taken one step further by decorating the

arches themselves with a brickwork pattern and the cyc with a backdrop of trees and flowers. This would provide fixed scenery suitable for all of the scenes in the play. Brickwork can be painted onto large sheets of lining paper and fixed to the arches to avoid any permanent disfiguration. A similar process would work with the scenery attached to the cyc, if it is also unfeasible to decorate that permanently. Just make sure that whatever you use to attach the scenery holds it on well!

● If you are performing the play on raised rostra – as many schools do – then you could create simple wooden or cardboard screens to act as the wings at the side of the stage and the back wall, and could decorate these with either brickwork or trees and flowers. Room dividers, or similar, work well. Again, these can remain static throughout the play and will act as a permanent backdrop for all of the scenes.

● If, however, you would like to change the scenery for each different setting you will require some form of changeable backdrop. If you're lucky enough to have a pulley system at your school, then use this to hang a painted backdrop. However, you are limited to the number of backdrops you can fit on the pulley system, so this method is not ideal.

Other options, therefore, include:

● Painting scenery onto large sheets of material and draping these over a long clothes rail (the type found in warehouses or large stores). These have castors and can easily be swung round to show the other side of any painted cloth – thus providing an instant scene change.

● Painting scenery onto large wooden or cardboard screens with castors attached and wheeling these on to provide a moveable backdrop.

● Asking any potential carpenters to make a large wooden frame – approximately 8' x 6'. Attach a large piece of muslin or cotton to it firmly, stretching the material tightly across and around the edge of the frame. Fix castors to the bottom and paint your scenery onto it. This can then be wheeled on to provide an instant backdrop. Material could be attached to both sides of the frame, providing you with two backdrops. The main problem then is getting these large screens on and off the stage and storing them when not in use.

● Fixing a long, detachable, pole across the back of the staging area and attaching several pieces of material with a different scene painted on each one. These can then be 'flipped over' as necessary

● Using the same detachable pole, but drawing the material, like curtains, across the back of the staging area – though it should be borne in mind that this will only provide one scenery change.

Whatever you choose, please remember two things:

● It is no great shame to select fixed scenery as an option. It is much better to spend what limited time and resources you have in creating a wonderfully elaborate setting that remains fixed, than to fail in trying to create a large variety of different scenery effects.

● Movable scenery needs someone to be responsible for bringing it on (at the right moment), taking it off (at the right moment), and somewhere for it to be stored when not in use.

Finally, create interesting effects by varying the entrances and exits of your actors. For example, the narrators in this play do not necessarily have to speak their lines from the stage, they can do this from any part of the hall and this can create an interesting diversion for the audience.

LIGHTING

Lighting in a play is used to establish time, enhance setting or create atmosphere. If you are lucky enough to have a professional lighting rig, you can really create some wonderful lighting effects. If not, simple lighting can often be sufficient to establish the basics. Our production of *A Suitably Happy Ending* was lit very simply with a 'general wash' – the stage was completely lit up. The action takes place over only one or two days, resulting in very few time changes in the play and allowing the lighting to remain constant throughout.

If you have a dimmer switch, use this to good effect – especially when Jack arrives at the Large and Spooky Forest. If you don't have the facility to dim lights, leave them on full for the whole play. Alternatively, you can switch off one or two lights to give the impression of a spooky atmosphere.

If you have a professional lighting rig, you could use coloured 'gels' to create some atmospheric lighting. These are transparencies which fit over your spotlights to give them a coloured glow. They must be purchased from a theatre lighting specialist because they need to be heat-resistant. A couple of spotlights with green gels attached combined with a couple of clear, white spotlights will give an excellent 'spooky forest' effect.

For a stage with no front curtains, lights can also be used to black out the stage during scene changes, or in preparation for the curtain call; but make sure that your actors practise moving around in the dark!

MUSIC AND SOUND EFFECTS

Music can be used effectively to set the scene. Choose any songs which highlight the themes of goblins, witches or fairy tales. Pick one as an opener and repeat it at the end of the play. This will act as a 'curtain', signalling to the audience when the play is starting and finishing.

Other musical extracts can be included at various points during the play:

- after the first section of narration
- between the end of SCENE 1 and the beginning of SCENE 2 – to illustrate the battle between the GOBLINS and the WITCHES
- at the point where JACK is banished from his home (something melancholy would work well).
- just before JACK enters the Large and Spooky Forest – to set the scene
- during the offstage battle between the GOBLINS and the WITCHES in SCENE 5
- an upbeat choral number at the end of the play.

It is also interesting to use music as a character theme – playing the same tune each time a specific character enters. However, this should really only be attempted with one or two characters and its use should be limited to avoid irritating the audience!

When choosing music, the obvious choices are usually the best but, if you have the time, try to search for a song or piece of music which reflects the context, or mood, rather than just picking up a general theme.

Before using music in a public performance, check that your school has the relevant licences to broadcast music at a public event.

If you don't want your actors to sing, other children in the school can be utilized as a chorus, seated around the staging area. They can sing the songs whilst those on stage mime appropriate actions.

Don't forget, also, to utilize your talented school musicians – both teachers and pupils! Music doesn't have to be tuneful or played from musical scores. Interesting musical sound effects can be created with a variety of unusual or home-made instruments. My big moment in a school production was providing the 'elephant' sounds on a baritone horn for a performance of *The Jungle Book*!

PROPS

Again, this play is very simple to stage and the only props which are essential are:

- walking sticks or crutches for the GOBLINS and WITCHES after the battle (SCENE 2)
- a tube of toothpaste without a lid (SCENE 2)
- two chairs for the family to sit on (SCENE 3)
- an envelope containing JACK's SATs results (SCENE 3)
- a pair of glasses for the QUEEN (Scene 4)
- something to make crashing and banging noises offstage during the second battle between the GOBLINS and WITCHES (SCENE 5).

Nothing else is essential, although I'm sure your Witches would enjoy carrying broomsticks – available in all good theatrical shops throughout the year. Your Goblins will probably argue for the use of swords for the battles they have to fight. Deter them from this by telling them that Goblins fight with magic, not with swords!

COSTUMES

Costumes for *A Suitably Happy Ending* are also very simple. If you have the time and skill to create elaborate costumes, then feel free to do so! If not, the following ideas worked perfectly well for our production:

Narrator: The narrator(s) should be dressed in their own (smart) clothes. If using more than one narrator, I feel that it is better to stipulate a colour scheme – either all in black and white or red and black, or similar. This is so that they are dressed in some form of recognizable 'costume' – and, more importantly, that they *feel* they are. Narrators need the thrill of 'dressing up' too!

Goblins: Dress these all in brown: leggings, jogging bottoms or tights, combined with T-shirts, sweatshirts, jumpers or tops. Either keep their feet bare (cut the feet off the tights) or put them in black plimsolls or ballet slippers. Do not let them wear tights or socks without shoes as that can be extremely dangerous. Jumpers should only be worn in an emergency – if nothing else is available – the combination of heat and excitement can make children physically ill and I've known one or two to faint! Pointed ears are a great addition to the Goblin costume – cut them out

of brown card or sugar paper and fix the two matching ear shapes together along the outside edge using double-sided tape. Slip the gap at the bottom over the child's own ear and that's it!

Witches: Dress them all in black: combining similar costume items as for the Goblins but with the addition of long black skirts or black dresses. The Witches should really wear black pumps, ballet slippers or shoes (*not* trainers), but leave them in bare feet if these are unavailable. Cloaks are a great addition to the costume. Many children will already have one at home, but they can be made simply using large pieces of black material which is either hemmed at one end and threaded with a black ribbon to tie it, or simply pinned or sewn onto the actor's other clothes at the shoulder. (Always pin from underneath to avoid too much metal showing.) Witches' hats should be made from black card or sugar paper formed into a cone. These can be gripped into the hair using black hairgrips, or black elastic can be threaded through two small holes to form a chin strap. However you make them, always use both glue and sticky tape for any join and check the hats after each performance if doing more than one – they have a habit of disintegrating!

Mother: Dress in a stereotypical 'mother' costume: floral skirt, blouse and tights. An apron is an option, but not one I'd choose! Shoes may be a problem, unless you have a child with large feet who has a mother with small feet! Otherwise, black pumps, ballet slippers or 'sensible' school shoes will be acceptable.

Father: Combine smart, or school, trousers (preferably black) with a white shirt and tie. Black

pumps or 'sensible' school shoes complete the image. Under no circumstances should the child playing Father be allowed to wear trainers!

Jack: Combine jeans, or dungarees, with a bright shirt or T-shirt. Boots or trainers can be worn by this character. The part can be played by a boy or girl (I cast a girl in my production) and this 'androgynous' costume works really well for either.

Brother: Again, dress the character in jeans but combine them with a dull shirt or T-shirt (to contrast with Jack's costume). This character can also wear trainers, but not boots.

Sisters 1 and 2: Dress them in long skirts or dresses combined with blouses, shirts or T-shirts. You must make sure that only Jack 'cross-dresses' – don't allow these females to wear jeans as well! School shoes, smart shoes, black pumps or ballet slippers are all acceptable as footwear.

Servants 1 and 2: Dress them in black trousers combined with smart white shirts and black bow ties. Stitch a piece of silver or gold ribbon or braid down the outside of each trouser leg. Put them in black plimsolls or smart black shoes and make silver or gold buckles by covering a buckle-shaped piece of cardboard with foil. Fix to the shoe with a safety pin, some thread, black elastic, or by using the shoe-lace. An alternative would be to dress them in knee-length trousers (which can be made by cutting a pair at the knee and hemming with elastic), and combining these with tights worn underneath, a smart shirt, bow tie

and bright waistcoat on top and the buckled shoes.

The Queen: Dress her in a beautiful, flowing dress in bright, colourful material. A cloak can be made simply from a gold-coloured curtain (or material), again hemmed and threaded with ribbon and tied around the neck, or pinned onto the shoulders. The crown I used was made from gold card cut out and stuck together – cut the crown spires before forming the crown shape! I then stuck little silver and gold stars all over it. It just about lasted through two performances! Alternatively, crowns and cloaks can be purchased quite cheaply at any good theatrical costumiers – and often in joke shops. She should wear ballet slippers, or flat shoes and, if possible, these should be gold or silver. If any children have any old, flat shoes they no longer wear, spray or dye them.

MAKE-UP

All make-up is dependent on the type of lighting used in your performance arena. If you are working under professional stage lights, then more make-up must be applied as these remove colour and contour from the face. If, however, you are working under school lights or strip lights, be very careful just to define features and express the characters. Water-based make-up is excellent for whole face coverage and grease-based for eyes, cheeks and lips. It is important to practise applying the make-up prior to the performances.

The make-up for *A Suitably Happy Ending* is quite simple, and very little is required. I would suggest the following:

Narrator: Narrator(s) should be made up with simple, light lipstick and eyeshadow. Try to prevent them from wearing too much as it isn't necessary. It's more important that they look clean, tidy and smart.

Goblins: Give them brown lips and line their eyes with brown eyeliner. This gives them a rather unpleasant appearance which is very effective!

Witches: Give them black lips and line their eyes with black eyeliner. Again, this works well.

You can use water-based all-over make-up for the Goblins and Witches – brown for the Goblins and Green for the Witches – but please remember that, once you start, every bit of bare flesh has to be covered!

Mother and Father: Mother and Father need a little bit of foundation all over their face, blue eyeshadow, a touch of blusher and a nice red or pink lipstick for Mother. If you want to give Father a bit of stubble, take a small, firm brush and cover it with black make-up (a black grease stick or similar) and tap it lightly end-on onto the face. Get the child to suck their lips in and apply just below the nose as well. Children will moan whilst it is being applied, but they love the effect. The main problem then is how to prevent them touching and smudging it!

Brother / Sister 1 and Sister 2: Keep it very simple, using basic foundation, blue eyeshadow, a little bit of blusher and a touch of pink or pale red lipstick. Any boys playing 'Brother' will complain, but they must have some make-up on to prevent their features from disappearing under the lights.

Servant 1 and Servant 2: Both Servants need a little bit of foundation all over their face, blue eyeshadow, a touch of blusher and light application of pale red or pink lipstick. An addition which works well is to draw on curly moustaches using a black eyeliner pencil. This takes practice, but can be very effective and the children love them!

The Queen: Use the same basic make-up as for Mother, but make the colours slightly stronger, or darker. The Queen should also be given a 'beauty spot' using a black eyeliner pencil.

If you want to 'age' your children, use a red-toned grease stick and a cocktail stick. Ask the children to screw up their faces and apply the grease paint into the wrinkles, using the cocktail stick. Think carefully about where wrinkles form on the face as you age and simply put them there. Be careful not to draw in too many lines, though, or the poor child will end up with a face like a road map!

LEARNING LINES

Children never fail to amaze me with their capacity for learning and retaining lines. However, everyone needs support in learning lines at some time and the following are some of the methods which can help:

REPETITION

This requires constant and regular reading of the script. Go over the children's lines again and again, and they'll learn them by rote. Using this method means that children often learn everyone else's lines as well, which is not a problem until they insist on prompting whilst on stage.

FROM CUES

Read the line immediately before theirs. Let them read their line out loud. Read the 'cue line' again, but this time cover up the child's line on the script. This way, they are learning the important cues as well as their own lines.

ON PAPER

Write each child's cue lines and own lines on a separate piece of paper, to prevent them being daunted by a large script. Use this method for children to learn one scene or short section at a time. They can carry the pieces of paper around with them, and will memorize the lines quite quickly by absorbing these short extracts.

ON TAPE

Help the children to read through the script two or three times. Record each child's cue lines on tape, leaving a long pause after each one for them to interject his or her own lines. Work through this with each child initially, using the script as an accompanying visual aid; then let them try it alone. Gradually remove their dependence on using the script, until they can say their lines in the recorded pauses without hesitating. Alternatively, you could record both the cue lines and their lines and then leave a gap for them to repeat their own lines.

VERBAL SUPPORT

Some children respond better to verbal support and learn lines by hearing them spoken and then simply repeating. However, this can take up an awful lot of your rehearsal time!

In addition, enlist the support of family members to help the children with learning their lines. Encourage children to 'test' each other and try to create an atmosphere of support. Don't be too worried if children paraphrase their lines, so long as important aspects of the script aren't omitted.

Use what literacy time you can to read through the script a number of times as a whole group. Try to balance the need for them to remember what they have to say, with not frightening them so much that they forget everything!

It is up to you whether you appoint a designated 'prompter'. I prefer not to use one, as children can rely too much on being fed lines and not on their own ability to learn them. If you decide to have someone prompting he or she should attend *all* rehearsals to be thoroughly familiar with the performance.

CALMING NERVES AND CHANNELLING ENERGY

Those children who become stressed and nervous about performing must be allowed to feel that they have a 'get out clause'. If possible, have another child in mind who can take over their lines and let them know that they don't *have* to perform if they really don't want to. I say this on a regular basis to the young children I direct; and however terrified they become, they always end up performing. I think this is because they know that taking part in the play is their choice and that they can pull out at any time.

Give the more 'energetic' (a euphemism for 'disruptive'!) children specific tasks to perform. I often involve these children in helping others to learn lines, making props and even applying make-up during rehearsals. Having a sense of responsibility about an important job will usually calm over-excited children. However, there is always the option of threatening to remove them from the play – and meaning it – if they don't calm down.

The trick is to keep all the children occupied. This prevents them from having time to be worried, and uses up spare energy. Use your rehearsal planning time to add two or three production-related tasks which can be done whilst rehearsals are in progress. Alternatively, bring drawing paper and crayons to rehearsals and ask children to draw the stage and set. I've also used word puzzles and colouring books and asked them to write and decorate invitations to their families to come and see the play. All obvious strategies, but they work!

CURTAIN CALLS

I've seen some terrible curtain calls which have completely spoiled an otherwise good performance. Bear in mind that this is the last memory your audience will have of the play, and that any sloppiness now will completely override any professionalism that may have gone before.

I'm not in favour of the 'pantomime-style' walk-down curtain calls, where the actors come on to take their bows one by one, to different audience responses. It isn't fair on those children who have taken on the less 'popular' parts.

A good way to structure curtain calls is as follows:

- Line up all of the children on stage in several rows according to height, with the tallest ones at the back. Space them out so they can all be seen.
- Tell the children to look around and notice who they are standing next to, in front of and behind.
- Ask them to stand upright, with their feet together and their hands resting lightly on the front of their thighs.
- Now nominate one child in the centre of the front row to start the bow. Tell all of the other children to watch this child carefully, without making their observation noticeable.
- When the nominated child on the front row bows slowly, everyone must bow. Bowing should be done from the waist, with hands sliding down to the knees and the eyes directed at the floor. Make sure that everyone moves at the same, slow pace – bowing too quickly can give the appearance of a group of nodding ducks!
- Tell the children to hold the bowing position for a slow count of 'two', then everyone should straighten up again.
- Repeat, with everyone following the front row leader again.

Finally – and essentially – make sure the children keep up the same level of professionalism when leaving the stage. Don't allow them to scream, shout, wave to their parents or whatever! A smooth, professional ending like this can really round off a lovely performance!

LITERACY SUPPORT

The following are some brief suggestions for literacy activities that could follow on from reading and performing the playscript.

STORY

Ask the children to retell the story. This can be done in a number of contexts:

● Assign sections to different groups and invite an oral retelling in sequence with the whole class as the audience.
● Storyboard the main events, with or without captions, in small groups or as a whole class.
● Ask individual children to record the main incidents in single sentences with accompanying pictures to create a 'wall story'.

As a class or in groups, write an additional scene for the play, continuing the story in scripted form and using the same style as the author.

Devise an alternative ending for the play, working as a whole class or in small groups, and improvise before recording in writing or on tape.

CHARACTERS

Ask the children to draw a picture of their favourite character and use at least three adjectives to write a description of them.

Groups or individuals can write a letter from Jack to his family which expresses his happiness about his life in the palace.

Help the children perform the play using simple puppets, paying particular attention to the voices for different characters and the narrator.

THEME

Ask the children to decide what they think the main theme of the play is (such as 'good triumphing over evil'). In small groups, improvise and then write a short play based on the same theme. The groups can perform their plays to the rest of the class.

The children can create a story about an argument which has serious consequences.

WORKING WITH PLAYSCRIPT LAYOUT

Explore the layout conventions of playscripts, using a short section of the text. Look together at how stage directions are written, how the scenes are structured, and so on. Explain these conventions.

Let the children practise laying out a playscript on a computer, using a familiar story and one or two pages of *A Suitably Happy Ending* on photocopiable pages 17–35 as a model.

Using the bracketed stage directions for character expression, can the children find and list at least five adverbs which have been formed using the suffix –ly (such as politely, hopefully, cheerfully)?

PERFORMANCE-RELATED TASKS

Invite the children to:

● write and design a programme for the play which gives all the relevant information to the audience
● design and draw a set for the play
● design and draw the costume for their least favourite character, explaining how the costume expresses the character's personality, the reasons for their choice of colours and materials and how the design reflects the setting of the play.